CHART
HITS

WISE PUBLICATIONS
PART OF THE MUSIC SALES GROUP
LONDON / NEW YORK / PARIS / SYDNEY / COPENHAGEN / BERLIN / MADRID / HONG KONG / TOKYO

ALSO AVAILABLE IN THE REALLY EASY PIANO SERIES...

ABBA
25 GREAT HITS. ORDER NO. AM980430

CHILDREN'S FAVOURITES
20 POPULAR HITS. ORDER NO. AM998745

CHRISTMAS
24 FESTIVE CHART HITS. ORDER NO. AM980496

CLASSICAL FAVOURITES
24 WELL-KNOWN FAVOURITES. ORDER NO. AM993366

COLDPLAY
20 SONGS FROM COLDPLAY. ORDER NO. AM1009547

ELTON JOHN
24 CLASSIC SONGS. ORDER NO. AM987844

FRANK SINATRA
21 CLASSIC SONGS. ORDER NO. AM987833

GREAT FILM SONGS
22 BIG FILM HITS. ORDER NO. AM993344

GREAT SHOWSTOPPERS
20 POPULAR STAGE SONGS. ORDER NO. AM993355

JAZZ GREATS
22 JAZZ FAVOURITES. ORDER NO. AM1000857

LOVE SONGS
22 CLASSIC LOVE SONGS. ORDER NO. AM989582

MICHAEL JACKSON
19 CLASSIC HITS. ORDER NO. AM1000604

MORE 21ST CENTURY HITS
21 POPULAR HITS. ORDER NO. AM996534

MOZART
22 CLASSICAL FAVOURITES. ORDER NO. AM1000648

NEW CHART HITS
19 BIG CHART HITS. ORDER NO. AM996523

NO. 1 HITS
22 POPULAR CLASSICS. ORDER NO. AM993388

POP HITS
22 GREAT SONGS. ORDER NO. AM980408

SHOWSTOPPERS
24 STAGE HITS. ORDER NO. AM982784

TV HITS
25 POPULAR HITS. ORDER NO. AM985435

60S HITS
25 CLASSIC HITS. ORDER NO. AM985402

70S HITS
25 CLASSIC SONGS. ORDER NO. AM985413

80S HITS
25 POPULAR HITS. ORDER NO. AM985424

90S HITS
24 POPULAR HITS. ORDER NO. AM987811

50 FABULOUS SONGS
FROM POP SONGS TO CLASSICAL THEMES. ORDER NO. AM999449

50 GREAT SONGS
FROM POP SONGS TO CLASSICAL THEMES. ORDER NO. AM995643

50 HIT SONGS
FROM POP HITS TO JAZZ CLASSICS. ORDER NO. AM1000615

PIANO TUTOR
FROM FIRST STEPS TO PLAYING IN A WIDE
RANGE OF STYLES — FAST!. ORDER NO. AM996303

ALL TITLES CONTAIN BACKGROUND NOTES FOR EACH SONG PLUS
PLAYING TIPS AND HINTS.

PUBLISHED BY
WISE PUBLICATIONS
14-15 BERNERS STREET, LONDON, W1T 3LJ, UK.

EXCLUSIVE DISTRIBUTORS:
MUSIC SALES LIMITED
DISTRIBUTION CENTRE, NEWMARKET ROAD, BURY ST EDMUNDS,
SUFFOLK, IP33 3YB, UK.
MUSIC SALES PTY LIMITED
LEVEL 4, 30-32 CARRINGTON STREET,
SYDNEY, NSW 2000 AUSTRALIA.

ORDER NO. AM1012033
ISBN 978-1-78558-437-4
THIS BOOK © COPYRIGHT 2016 BY WISE PUBLICATIONS,
A DIVISION OF MUSIC SALES LIMITED.

MUSIC ARRANGED BY FIONA BOLTON.
MUSIC ENGRAVED BY SARAH LOFTHOUSE, SEL MUSIC ART LTD.
COMPILED AND EDITED BY NAOMI COOK.
PRINTED IN THE EU.

YOUR GUARANTEE OF QUALITY
AS PUBLISHERS, WE STRIVE TO PRODUCE EVERY BOOK TO THE HIGHEST
COMMERCIAL STANDARDS. THE MUSIC HAS BEEN FRESHLY ENGRAVED AND
THE BOOK HAS BEEN CAREFULLY DESIGNED TO MINIMISE AWKWARD PAGE
TURNS AND TO MAKE PLAYING FROM IT A REAL PLEASURE.
PARTICULAR CARE HAS BEEN GIVEN TO SPECIFYING ACID-FREE, NEUTRAL-
SIZED PAPER MADE FROM PULPS WHICH HAVE NOT BEEN ELEMENTAL
CHLORINE BLEACHED. THIS PULP IS FROM FARMED SUSTAINABLE FORESTS
AND WAS PRODUCED WITH SPECIAL REGARD FOR THE ENVIRONMENT.
THROUGHOUT, THE PRINTING AND BINDING HAVE BEEN PLANNED TO
ENSURE A STURDY, ATTRACTIVE PUBLICATION WHICH SHOULD GIVE YEARS
OF ENJOYMENT. IF YOUR COPY FAILS TO MEET OUR HIGH STANDARDS,
PLEASE INFORM US AND WE WILL GLADLY REPLACE IT.

WWW.MUSICSALES.COM

REALLY EASY PIANO

#3 AUTUMN/WINTER 2016

CHART HITS

Can't Stop The Feeling

Words & Music by Justin Timberlake, Max Martin & Shellback

Justin Timberlake's funky, disco-inspired pop hit was written for the 2016 animated film *Trolls*, for which Timberlake acted as executive music producer. The song marks a return to the charts for the star, putting him back in the US number one spot after nine years.

Hints & Tips: Try practising the left-hand part in the chorus separately to establish a solid disco feel before adding the syncopated melody.

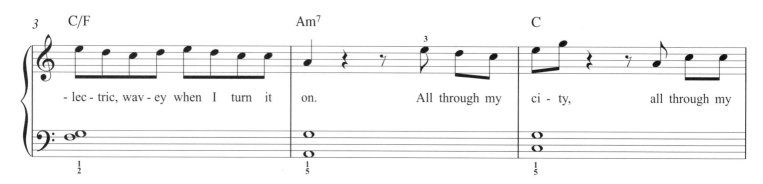

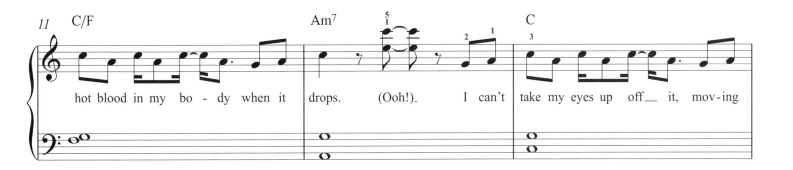

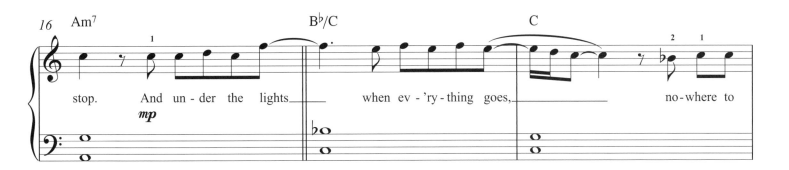

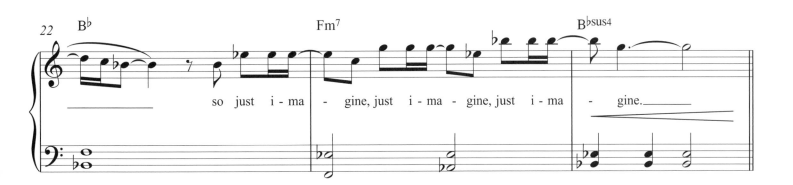

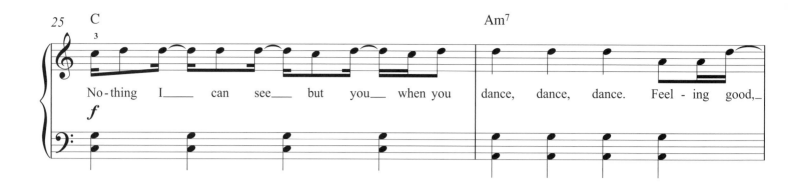

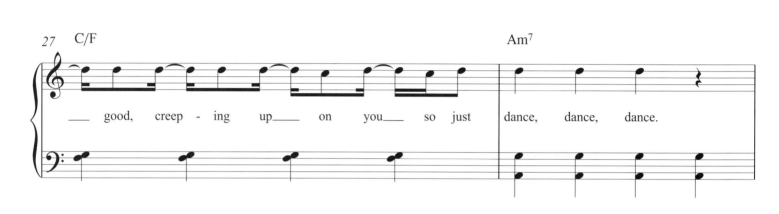

Charlemagne

Words & Music by Joseph Donovan, Charles Salt, Joshua Dewhurst, Thomas Ogden & Myles Kellock

'Charlemagne' is an electro-pop tune by indie band Blossoms, who were one of only two guitar bands to make the BBC's *Sound Of 2016* list. Their self-titled album hit number one on the UK Albums Chart and the band have been heralded as a brilliant blend of pop, rock, indie and electro.

Hints & Tips: The left hand has an interesting bass line in the verse – practise this separately before introducing the right hand.

Cold Water

Words & Music by Jamie Scott, Thomas Pentz, Benjamin Levin, Justin Bieber, Ed Sheeran, Philip Meckseper, Henry Allen & Karen Orsted

This relaxed, guitar-based tune features an all-star cast of Major Lazer, Justin Bieber and Danish singer MØ, with Ed Sheeran taking the writing credits. Producer Diplo said that as soon as he heard this tune, he knew it was perfect.

Hints & Tips: The first four phrases in the right hand have slightly unpredictable rhythms – clap them through first until you're confident.

Dancing On My Own

Words & Music by Robyn & Patrik Berger

This tale of heartache was originally penned by Swedish pop sensation Robyn. British singer Calum Scott has since made it his own after performing it as part of his audition for *Britain's Got Talent* in 2015. The original audition video has been watched over 73 million times.

Hints & Tips: This is a ballad: work on making the left hand steady and smooth and getting the notes on the word 'oh' in bars 23 and 27 nice and *legato*.

Good Grief

Words & Music by Daniel Smith & Mark Crew

The first single from Bastille's hotly-anticipated second album, 'Good Grief' is a catchy pop-rock tune about how bizarre grief and loss can be. The video for the song features a series of strange and colourful images of different people, as well as frontman Dan Smith's disembodied head singing on the floor.

Hints & Tips: There are lots of dynamic changes in this song – make the most of them! Watch out for the chord changes in the left hand in the chorus (from bar 13).

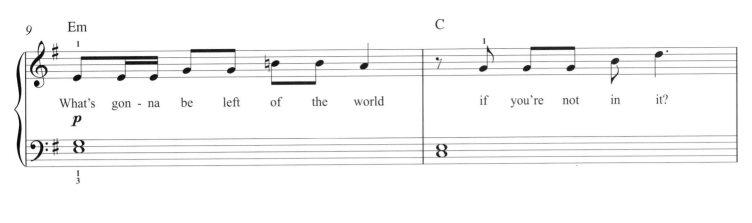

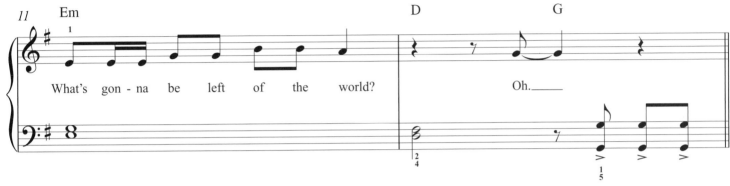

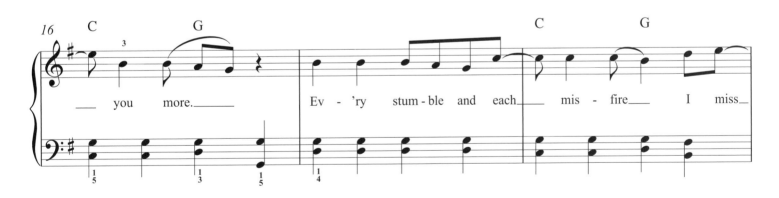

Hymn For The Weekend

Words & Music by Guy Berryman, Mikkel Eriksen, Chris Martin, Jon Buckland, Will Champion,
Tor Erik Hermansen, Venor Timothy Yard, Scott Alan Zant & Marcus Tovar

The second single from Coldplay's seventh studio album, this song was originally conceived by lead singer Chris Martin as a 'party song' but, with the help of the rest of the band, the focus moved to the idea of having an angelic person in your life, which ultimately resulted in Beyoncé singing on the track.

Hints & Tips: The left hand plays thirds from bar 17 – be sure to bring your fingers down on the keys at the same time so the two notes sound exactly together.

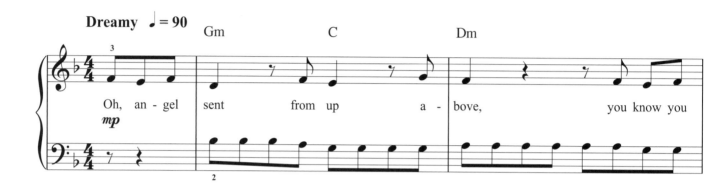

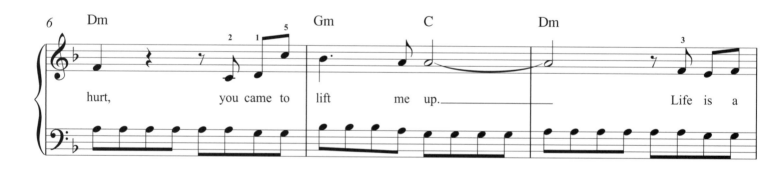

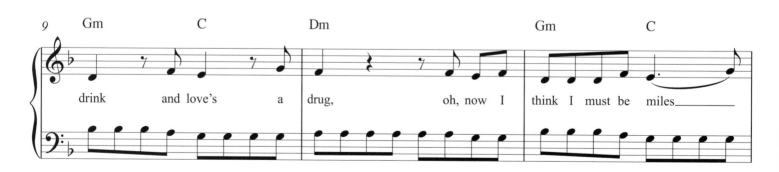

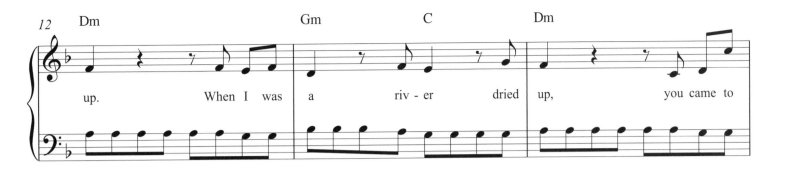

Just Like Fire

Words & Music by Max Martin, Alecia Moore, Shellback & Oscar Holter

Written for Disney's film *Alice Through The Looking Glass*, this song is a celebration of individuality. The music video incorporates many themes from the book, including the mirror, the chessboard and the Mad Hatter's tea party.

Hints & Tips: The left hand has the same pattern throughout, but it's quite syncopated so practise it on its own until you feel secure enough to introduce the right hand.

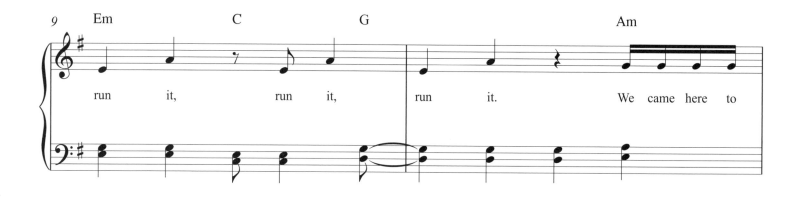

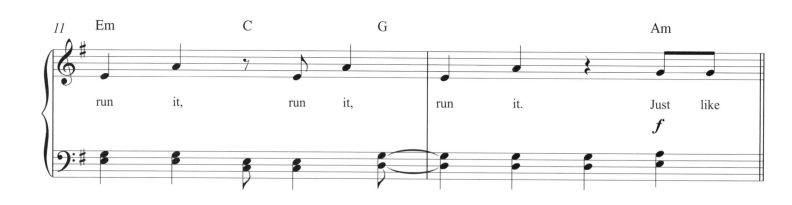

Into You

Words & Music by Savan Kotecha, Max Martin, Alexander Kronlund, Ilya & Ariana Grande

The second single from Grande's third album *Dangerous Woman*, this electro-pop anthem showcases the former child-star's impressive range. The song became her sixth UK Top 20 single and helped propel the album to its number one spot.

Hints & Tips: This is marked as 'pulsing' so make sure you keep a steady beat with the left hand crotchets. Notice that the phrases in the chorus all end on semiquavers – keep them short!

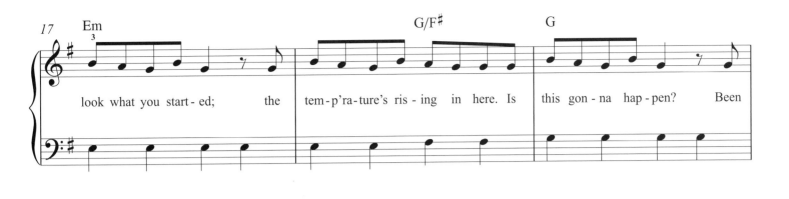

look what you start-ed; the tem-p'ra-ture's ris-ing in here. Is this gon-na hap-pen? Been

wait-ing and wait-ing for you to make a move,_ be-fore I make a move._

So ba-by, come light me up and may-be I'll let you on it. A

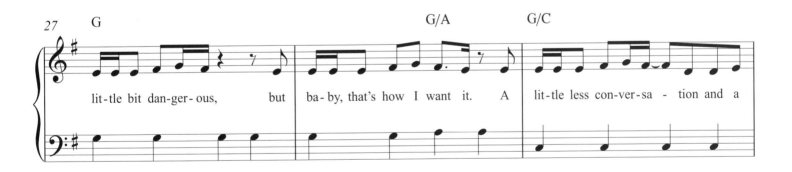

lit-tle bit dan-ger-ous, but ba-by, that's how I want it. A lit-tle less con-ver-sa - tion and a

lit-tle more touch my bo-dy, 'cause I'm so in - to you, in - to you, in - to you.

Lush Life

Words & Music by Markus Sepehrmanesh, Fridolin Walcher, Christoph Bauss, Iman Hulten, Linnea Soedal & Emanuel Abrahamsson

This upbeat, electro-pop tune by Swedish singer Zara Larsson is about breaking up with someone but still being positive and enjoying life. The song was Larsson's second number one in Sweden, topping the charts for five weeks, and it also reached number three in the UK.

Hints & Tips: As with 'Just Like Fire', the left hand has syncopated rhythms that may take some getting used to. Once secure, build up to introducing the right hand by speaking the words in rhythm first.

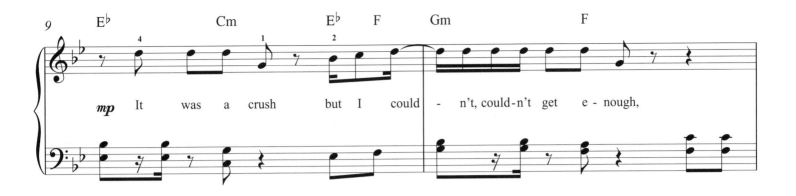

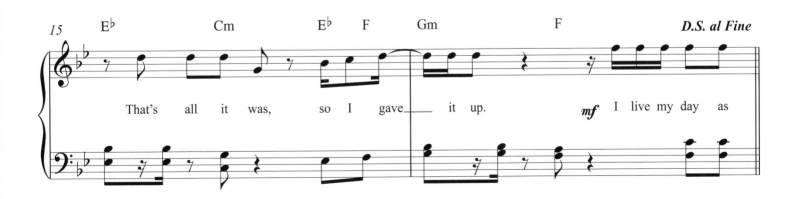

One Dance

**Words & Music by Aubrey Graham, Noah Shebib, Anthony Jefferies,
Ayodeji Balogun, Errol Reid, Kyla Smith & Luke Reid**

'One Dance' features Nigerian singer Wizkid and UK singer Kyla, who, when she heard Drake wanted to collaborate, thought it was an April Fool. No stranger to the UK underground scene, Drake is influenced by grime and is friends with rapper Skepta.

Hints & Tips: Practise the off-beat rhythms in bars 13-16 by tapping crotchets with your foot and clapping the right-hand part.

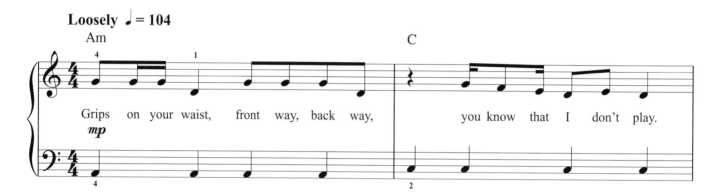

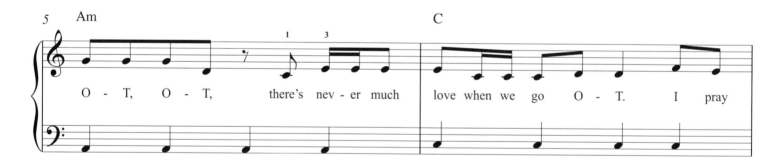

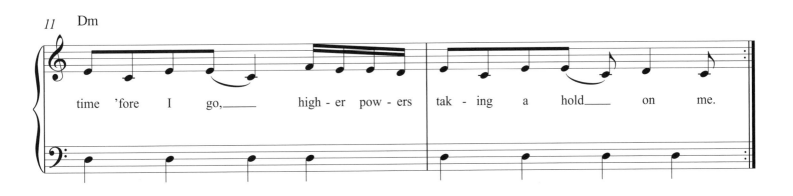

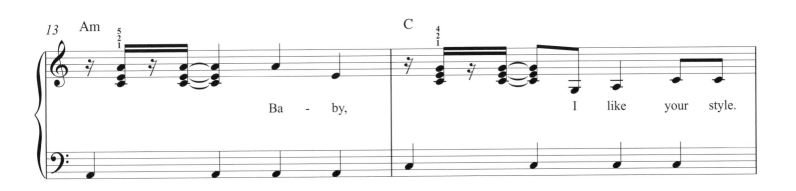

Perfect Strangers

Words & Music by Alex Smith, John Cooper & Guy Robin

'Perfect Strangers' is the follow-up to Jonas Blue's breakthrough 'Fast Car', a dance rework of the classic by Tracy Chapman. He wrote the chord progression soon after finishing the previous hit but it remained an instrumental until they found the ideal vocalist in JP Cooper, who brings a soulful feel to the song.

Hints & Tips: Bars 3, 11, 15 and 27 feature the left hand: use the finger indications to help you get the phrases nice and smooth.

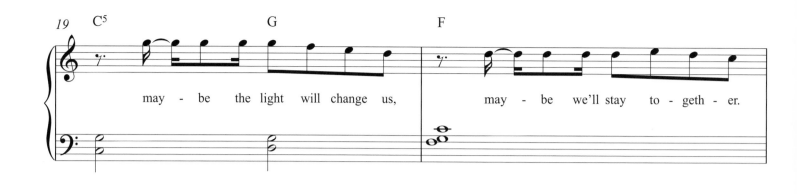

may - be the light will change us, may - be we'll stay to - geth - er.

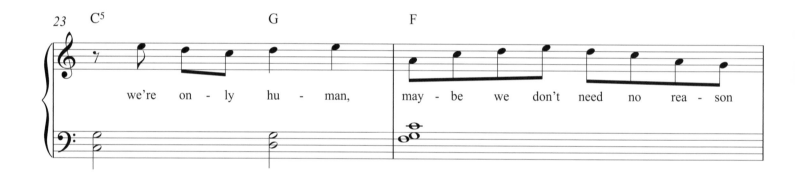

May - be we'll walk a - way, may - be we'll re - a - lise

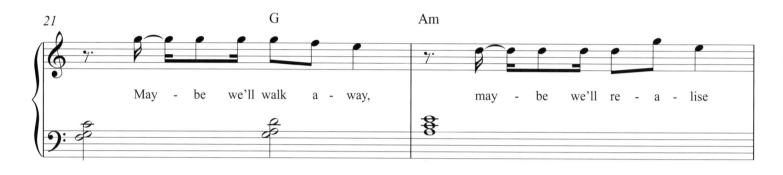

we're on - ly hu - man, may - be we don't need no rea - son

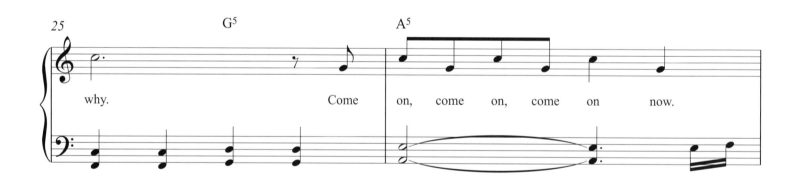

why. Come on, come on, come on now.

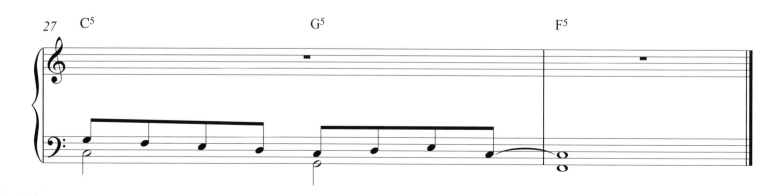

Tears

Words & Music by Jack Patterson & Samuel Roman

After taking the world by storm with their first album, Clean Bandit's second has this piano-led electro tune as its opening single. The song features a strong vocal performance by British singer and winner of *The X Factor* 2015, Louisa Johnson.

Hints & Tips: The melody consists mostly of triplets from bar 17 – try to imagine these rhythms in your head in bar 16 so you're prepared to play them in time.

Send My Love
(To Your New Lover)

Words & Music by Adele Adkins, Max Martin & Shellback

Beginning with a calypso-inspired guitar riff, this song sees Adele address her ex-partner directly, letting him know that she's over their relationship and completely moved on. The music video was shot over 12 takes, with various layers of Adele dancing creating a ghostly effect.

Hints & Tips: There are double notes from bar 9 – practise these slowly at first to help you get used to the jumps.

This Girl

Words & Music by Jake Mason, Lance Ferguson & Ivan Khatchoyan

French DJ and producer Kungs remixed a contemporary soul classic by Australian funk trio Cookin' On 3 Burners. The band have been active in the funk and soul scene for many years, but this remix propelled them to greater heights, peaking at number two in the UK charts and reaching the top spot in a number of European countries.

Hints & Tips: Use the finger markings to help you with the left hand part, which moves around quite a lot. Make sure both hands are exactly together from bar 17.

Too Good

Words & Music by Robyn Fenty, Aubrey Graham, Paul Jefferies, A. Martin,
Maneesh Bidaye & Dwayne Chin-Quee

The fourth collaboration between Drake and Rihanna sees the pair play a couple discussing their relationship and feelings. Another hit for the two, the driving drum beat supports some subtle guitar picking, brilliantly produced by Nineteen85.

Hints & Tips: Some of the right hand phrases roll into the next one without any rests – be ready to continue playing in bars 24 and 28. Remember there are two sharps too!

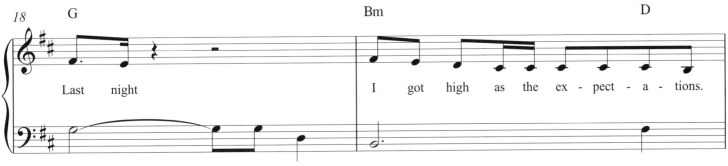

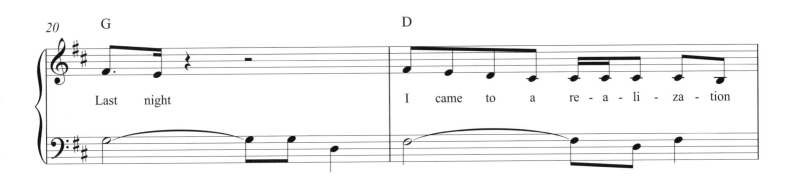

Treat You Better

Words & Music by Teddy Geiger, Shawn Mendes & Scott Harris

Written by Canadian singer-songwriter Shawn Mendes along with Scott Harris and Teddy Geiger, this was the lead single from his second album, *Illuminate*. The song was originally a reggae tune, but was changed just before the demo was recorded, although the guitar part still carries that instantly-recognisable rhythm.

Hints & Tips: The chorus from bar 16 has lots of double notes – practise these on their own, concentrating on keep them exactly together.

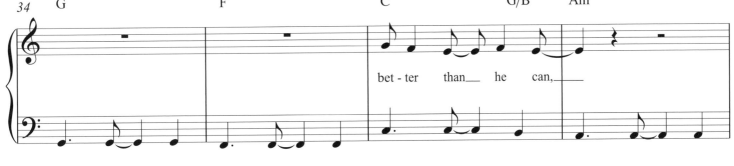

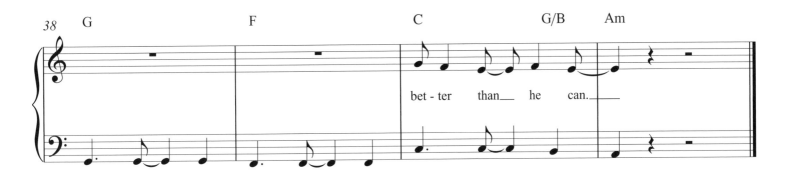

Work From Home

Words & Music by Joshua Coleman, Brian Lee, Alexander Izquiedro, Tyrone Griffin, Dallas Koehlke & Claire Demorest

This song was originally titled simply 'Work' but the group had to change it after Rihanna released her chart hit of the same name. Fifth Harmony auditioned as soloists on *The X Factor*, but were placed in a group by Simon Cowell.

Hints & Tips: There are some fast semiquaver passages in the chorus – practise the section from the end of bar 16 slowly until you can play confidently at the written tempo.

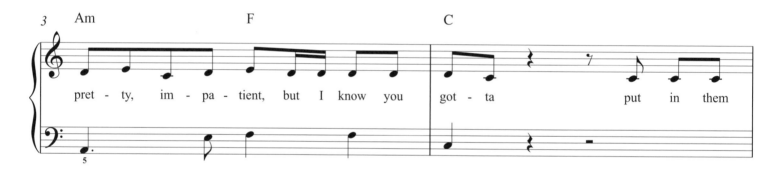

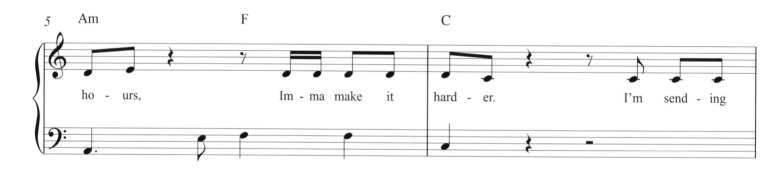

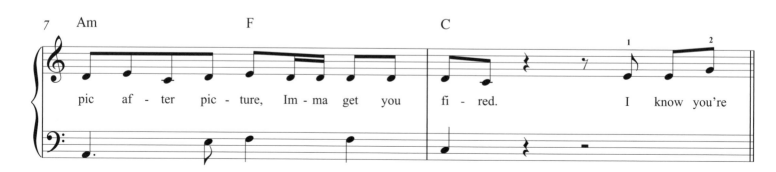

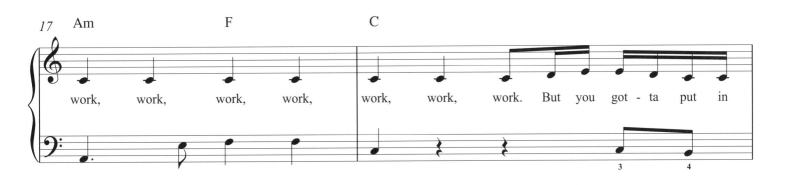

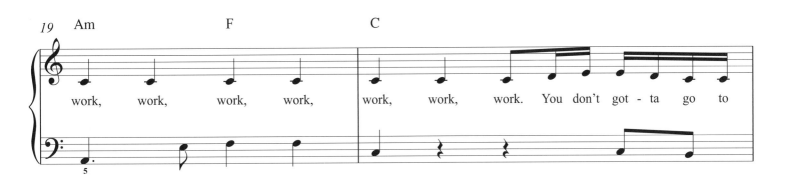

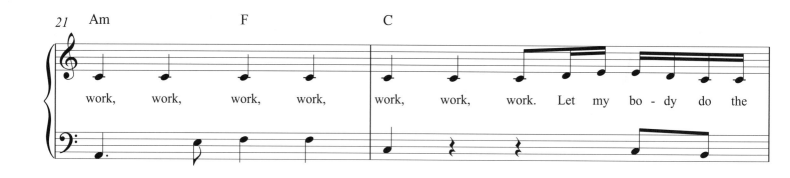

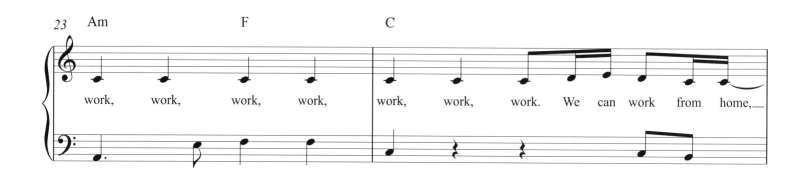

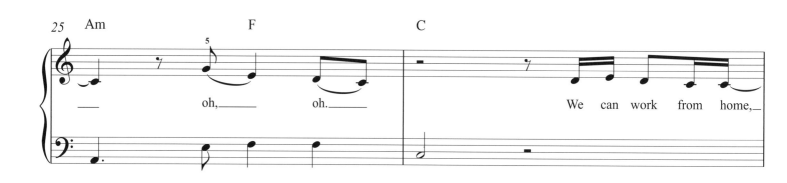

COLLECT THE SERIES...

CHART HITS

21 BIG CHART HITS FEATURING SONGS SUCH AS DO YOU KNOW?, HOLD ON, HOMETOWN GLORY, LOST, RUBY AND WHEN YOU'RE GONE.
ORDER NO. AM993377

GREAT FILM SONGS

22 GREAT FILM SONGS, INCLUDING; BLUE VELVET, HALLELUJAH, I WALK THE LINE, KNOCKIN' ON HEAVEN'S DOOR AND ONE DAY I'LL FLY AWAY.
ORDER NO. AM993344

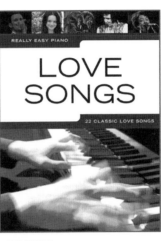

LOVE SONGS

22 POPULAR LOVE SONGS WITH HITS SUCH AS AIN'T NO SUNSHINE, CRAZY, FEVER, HAVE I TOLD YOU LATELY, LIKE A STAR AND LOVE ME TENDER.
ORDER NO. AM989582

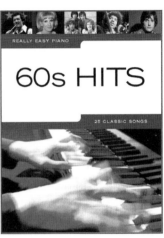

60s HITS

25 CLASSIC HITS, INCLUDING; CALIFORNIA DREAMIN', MY GENERATION, SON OF A PREACHER MAN, UNCHAINED MELODY AND WILD THING.
ORDER NO. AM985402

OVER 30 TITLES AVAILABLE...

REALLY EASY PIANO: ABBA
AM980430

REALLY EASY PIANO: BALLADS
AM982751

REALLY EASY PIANO: THE BEATLES
NO91080

REALLY EASY PIANO: CHRISTMAS
AM980496

REALLY EASY PIANO: CHRISTMAS CAROLS
AM985446

REALLY EASY PIANO: CLASSICAL
AM980419

REALLY EASY PIANO: CLASSICAL FAVOURITES
AM993366

REALLY EASY PIANO: COLDPLAY
AM1009547

REALLY EASY PIANO: ELTON JOHN
AM987844

REALLY EASY PIANO: FILM SONGS
AM980441

REALLY EASY PIANO: FILM THEMES
AM982762

REALLY EASY PIANO: FRANK SINATRA
AM987833

REALLY EASY PIANO: GERSHWIN
AM997249

REALLY EASY PIANO: JAZZ
AM982773

REALLY EASY PIANO: NEW CHART HITS
AM996523

REALLY EASY PIANO: NO.1 HITS
AM993388

REALLY EASY PIANO: POP HITS
AM980408

REALLY EASY PIANO: GREAT SHOWSTOPPERS
AM993355

REALLY EASY PIANO: SHOWSTOPPERS
AM982784

REALLY EASY PIANO: TV HITS
AM985435

REALLY EASY PIANO: 70S HITS
AM985413

REALLY EASY PIANO: 80S HITS
AM985424

REALLY EASY PIANO: 90S HITS
AM987811

REALLY EASY PIANO: 21ST CENTURY HITS
AM987822

...PLUS MANY MORE!

Whatever you want...

Music Sales publishes the very best in printed music for rock & pop, jazz, blues, country and classical as well as songs from all the great stage musicals.

Many of our practical publications come with helpful CDs or exclusive download links to music files for backing tracks and other audio extras.

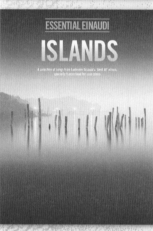

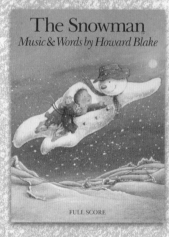

We also publish a range of tuition titles, books for audition use and book+DVD master classes that let you learn from the world's greatest performers.

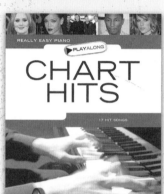

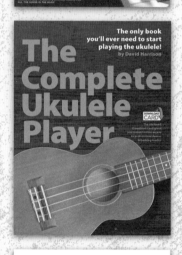

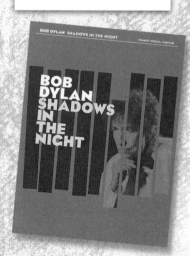

So, whatever you want, Music Sales has it.

Just visit your local music shop and ask to see our huge range of music in print.

In case of difficulty, contact marketing@musicsales.co.uk